SPMG

HEINEMANN MATHEMATICS 1

Name

WORKBOOK 4

Number to 10 : Relationships

Revised

How much?

Bus
ticket
p

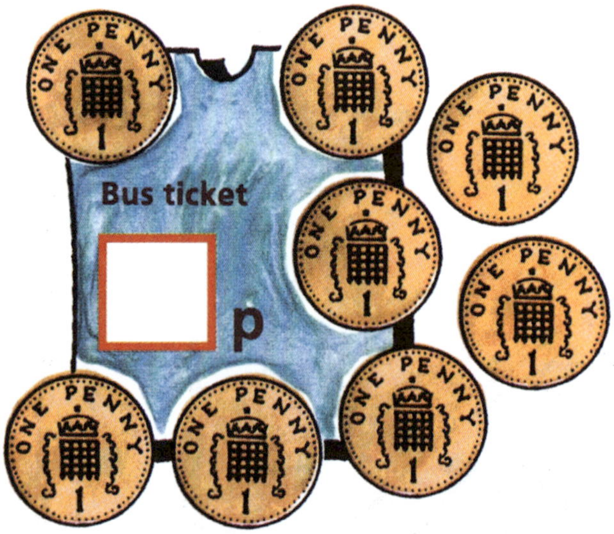
Bus ticket
p

Bus ticket
p

Bus
ticket
p

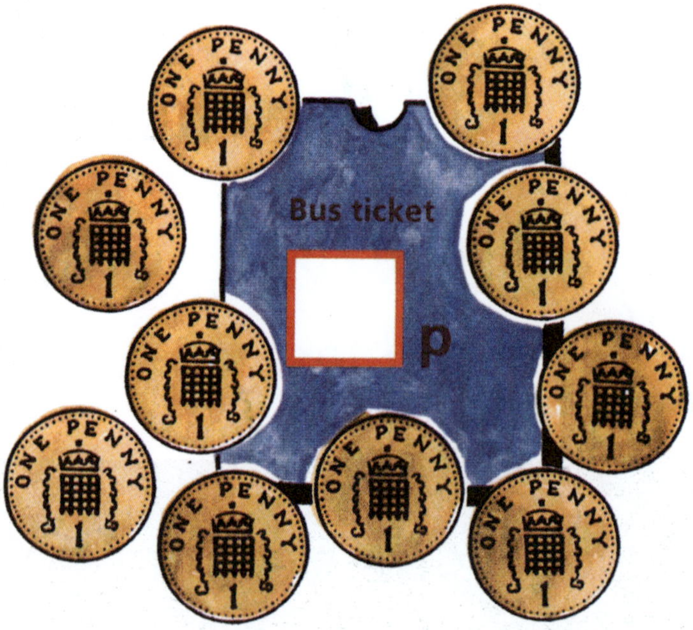
Bus ticket
p

Bus tickets

Jan has ☐ p

Can she buy Bus ticket 7 p ? ☐

Sam has ☐ p

Can he buy Bus ticket 8 p ? ☐

Jess has ☐ p

Can she buy Bus ticket 10 p ? ☐

Join the dots.

1 to 10

Bees

1 2 3 4 5 6 7 8 9 10

Write the number

after 3

after 6

after 9

after 5

before 2

before 8

Flower garden

Ring the one that is different.

On the

beach

6	7	8	9	10
six	seven	eight	nine	ten

How many?

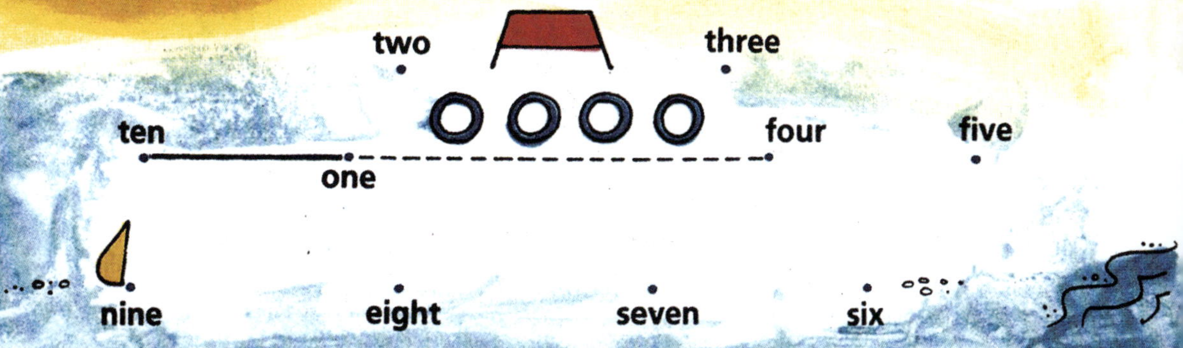

Cooks

2
two
eight
four
ten
six
three
one
five
nine
seven

ten
one
seven
nine
two
eight
three
six
five
four

Colour the first red, the second blue, and the third green.

Match

has a →

Sam

Pam

Ali

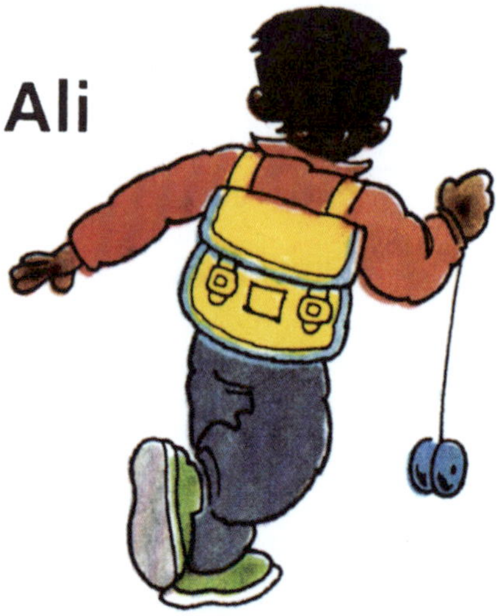

Colour the clothes

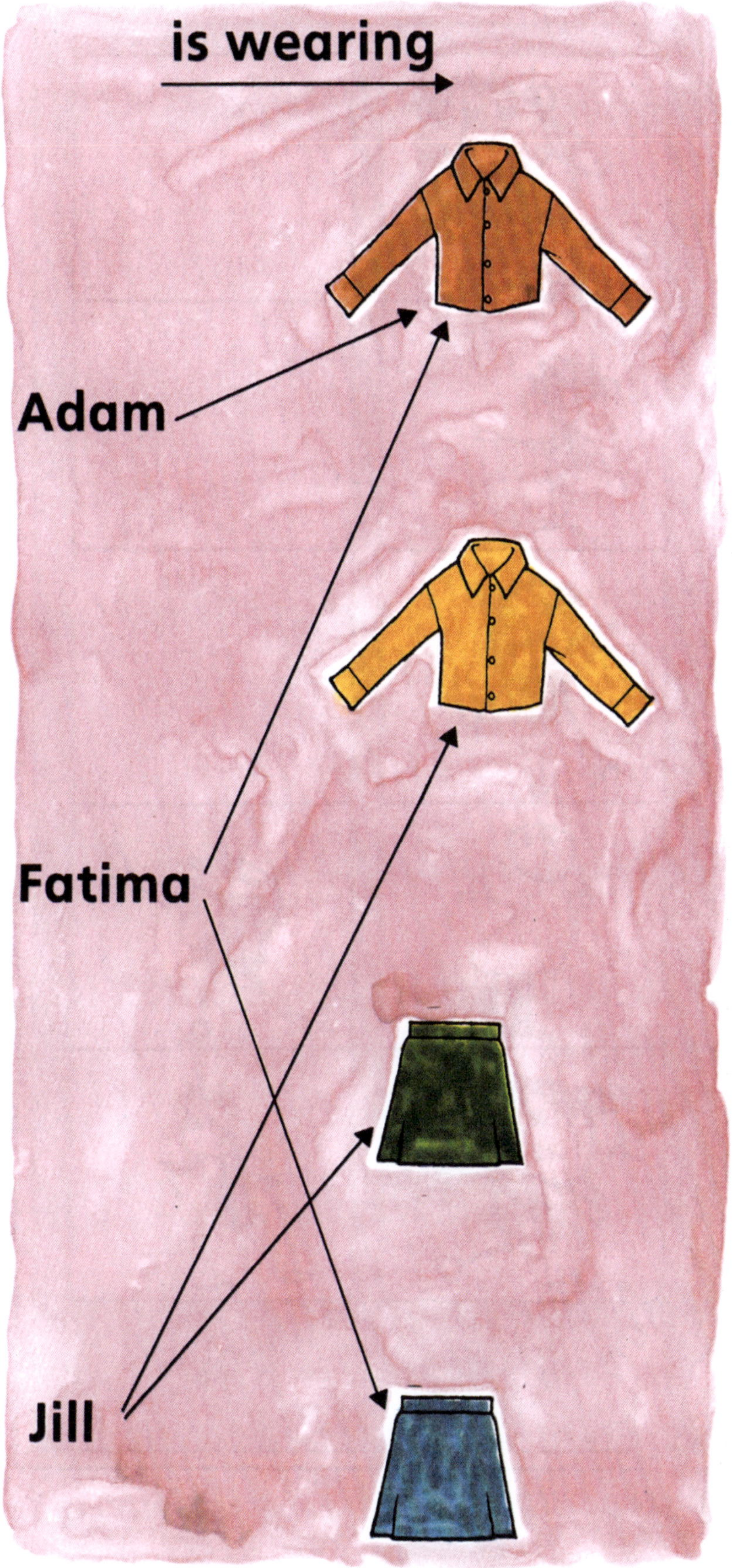

Our group

How many

girls ☐

boys ☐ ?

Draw one more boy.

How many boys now?

☐

Spots

How many?

black spots 2

blue spots

red spots

Draw my blue spots and my red spots.

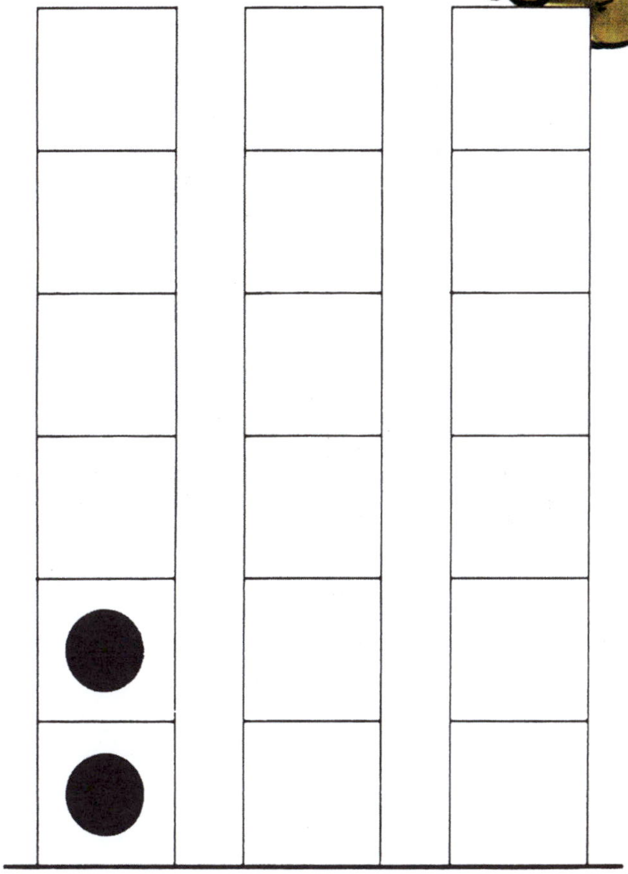

1p coins

Colour 1p coins to buy.

1	2	3	4	5	6	7	8	9	10	11	12	13	14	15

Heinemann is an imprint of Pearson Education Limited, a company incorporated in England and Wales, having its registered office at Edinburgh Gate, Harlow, Essex, CM20 2JE.
Registered company number: 872828
ISBN 978 0 435 03085 8
First published 1991. Revised edition 1995. 22 30
Typeset and illustrated by Oxprint Design.

ISBN 978-0-435030-85-8

SPMG

HEINEMANN MATHEMATICS 1

Name

WORKBOOK 4

Number to 10 : Relationships

How much?

Bus
ticket
p

Bus ticket
p

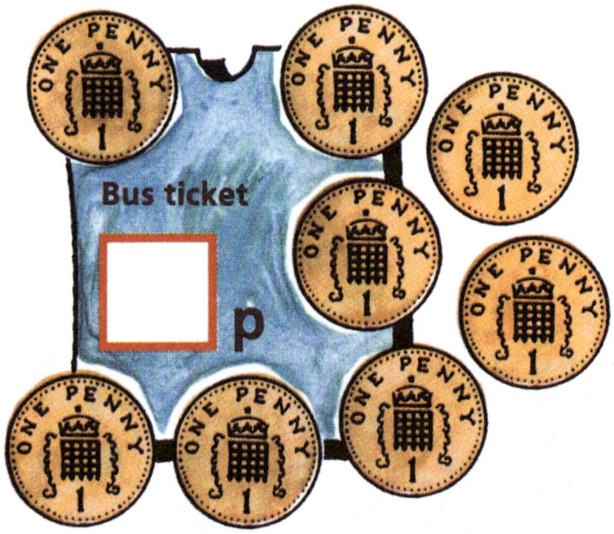
Bus ticket
p

Bus
ticket
p

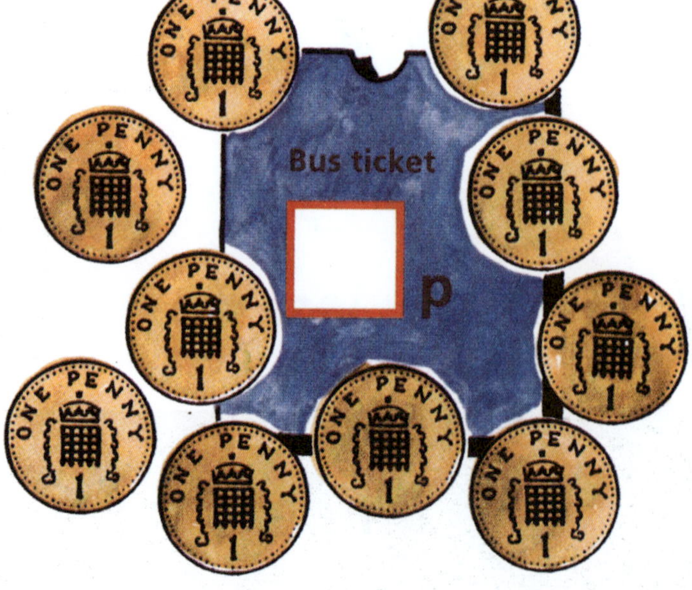
Bus ticket
p

Bus tickets

Jan has ☐ p

Can she buy

? ☐

Sam has ☐ p

Can he buy

? ☐

Jess has ☐ p

Can she buy

? ☐

Join the dots.

1 to 10

Bees

1 2 3 4 5 6 7 8 9 10

Write the number

after 3

after 6

after 9

after 5

before 2

before 8

Flower garden

Ring the one that is different.

On the

beach

How many?

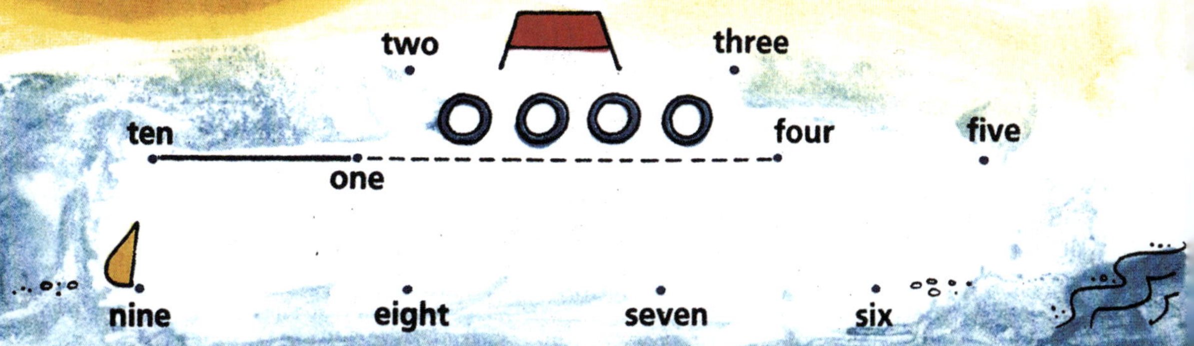

Cooks

2
two
eight
four
ten
six
three
one
five
nine
seven

ten
one
seven
nine
two
eight
six
three
five
four

Colour the first red, the second blue, and the third green.

Match

has a

Sam

Pam

Ali

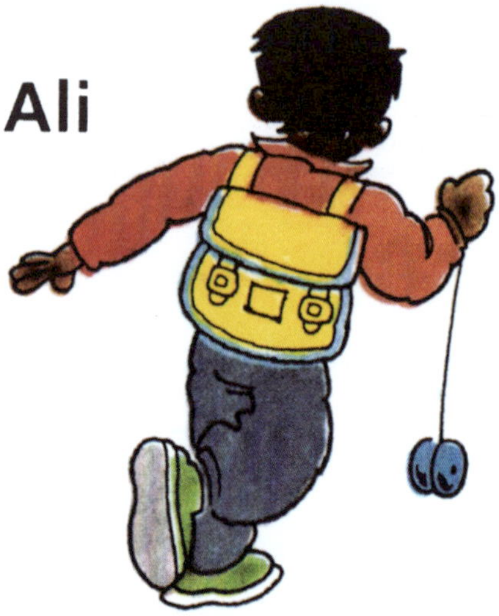

Colour the clothes

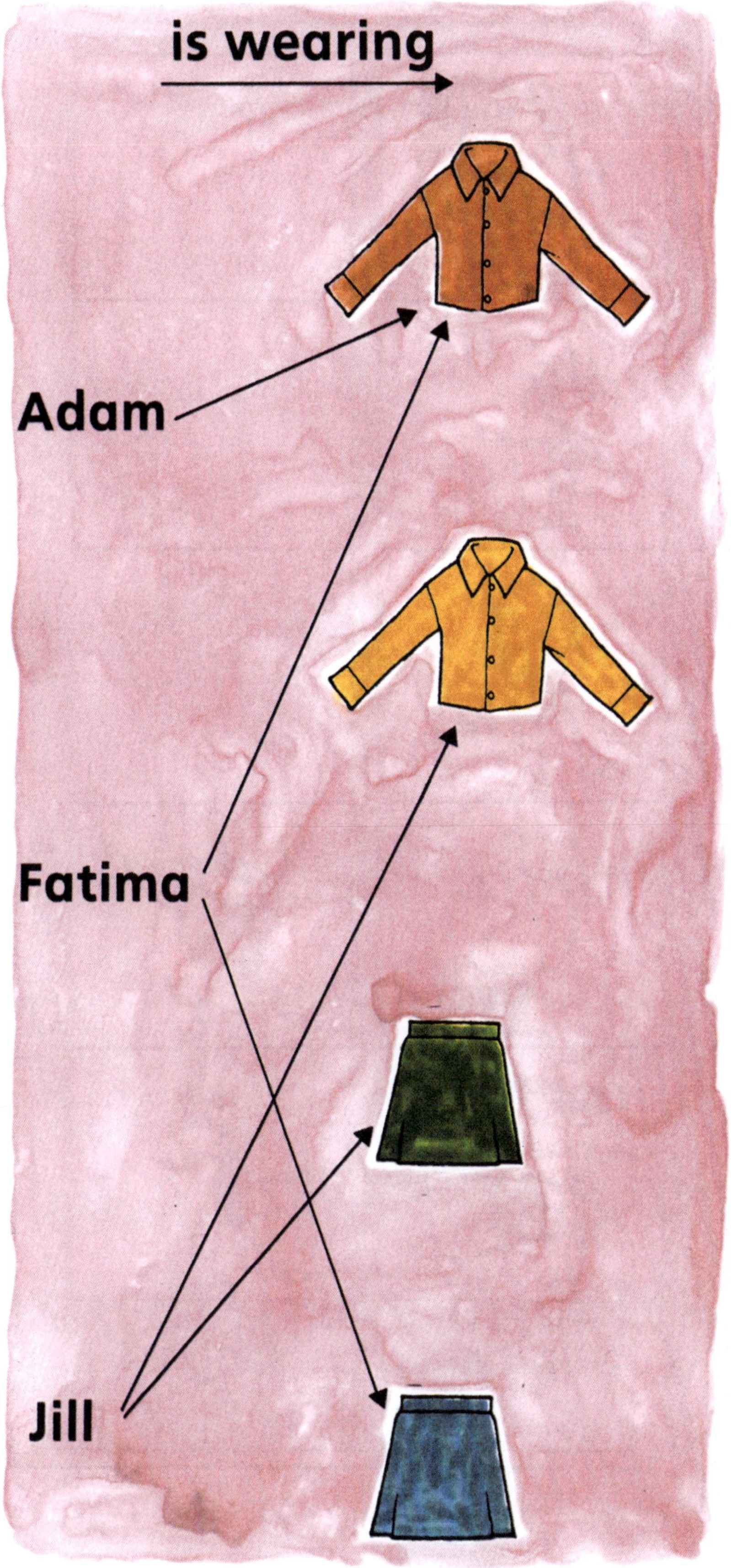

Adam

Fatima

Jill

Our group

How many

girls ☐

boys ☐ ?

Draw one more boy.

How many boys now?

☐

Spots

How many?

black spots	2
blue spots	
red spots	

Draw my blue spots and my red spots.

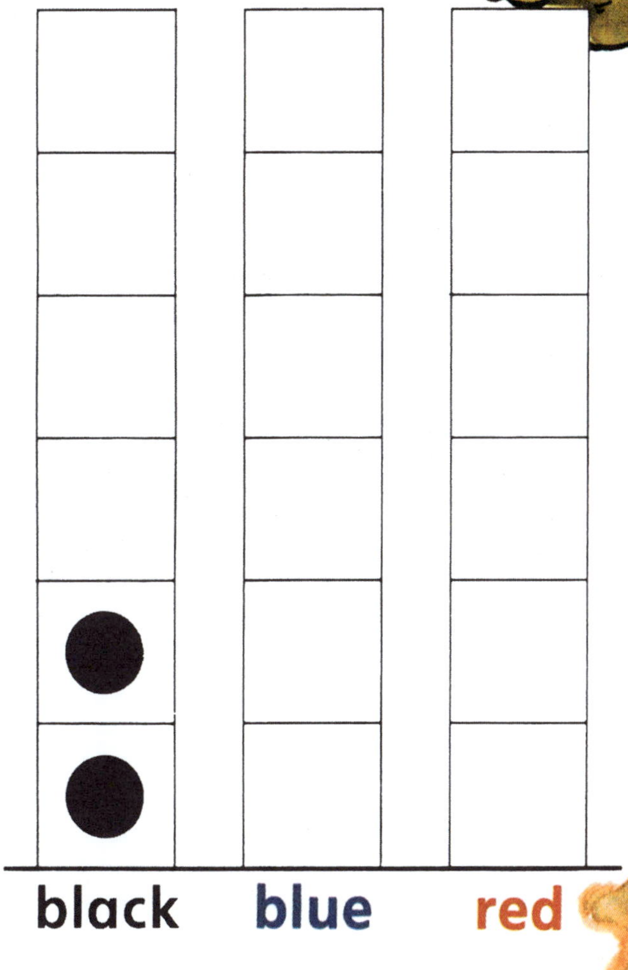

1p coins

Colour 1p coins to buy.

1	2	3	4	5	6	7	8	9	10	11	12	13	14	15

Heinemann is an imprint of Pearson Education Limited, a company incorporated in England and Wales, having its registered office at Edinburgh Gate, Harlow, Essex, CM20 2JE.
Registered company number: 872828
ISBN 978 0 435 03085 8
First published 1991. Revised edition 1995. 22 30
Typeset and illustrated by Oxprint Design.

ISBN 978-0-435030-85-8

SPMG

HEINEMANN MATHEMATICS 1

Name

WORKBOOK 4

Number to 10 : Relationships

Revised

How much?

Bus
ticket
p

Bus ticket
p

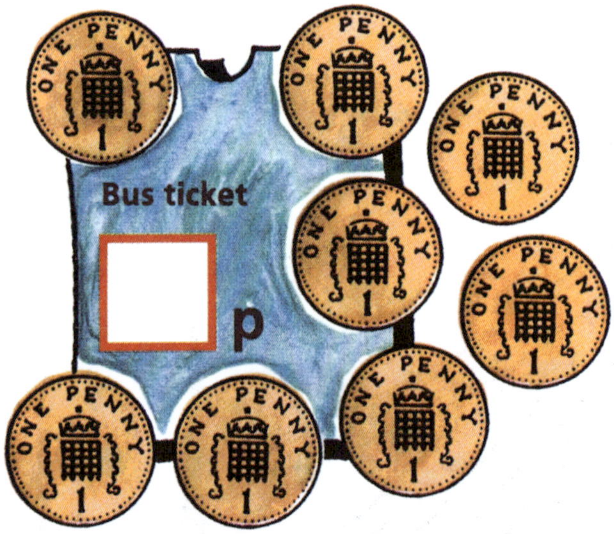
Bus ticket
p

Bus
ticket
p

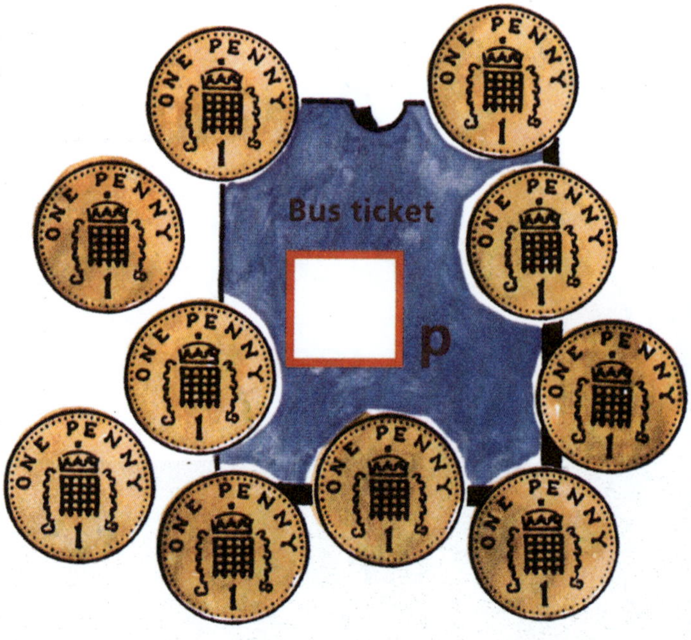
Bus ticket
p

Bus tickets

Jan has ____ p

Can she buy

? ____

Sam has ____ p

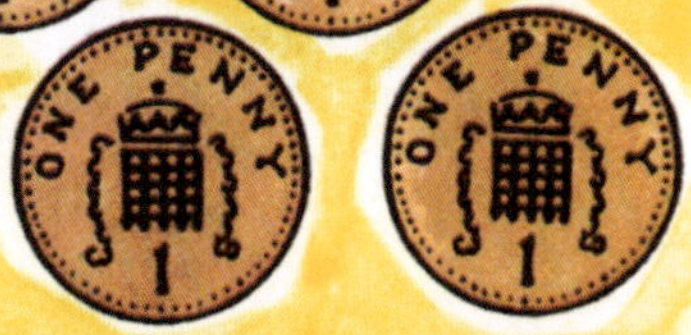

Can he buy

? ____

Jess has ____ p

Can she buy

? ____

Join the dots.

1 to 10

Bees

1 2 3 4 5 6 7 8 9 10

Write the number

after 3

after 6

after 9

after 5

before 2

before 8

Flower garden

Ring the one that is different.

On the

beach

6	7	8	9	10
six	seven	eight	nine	ten

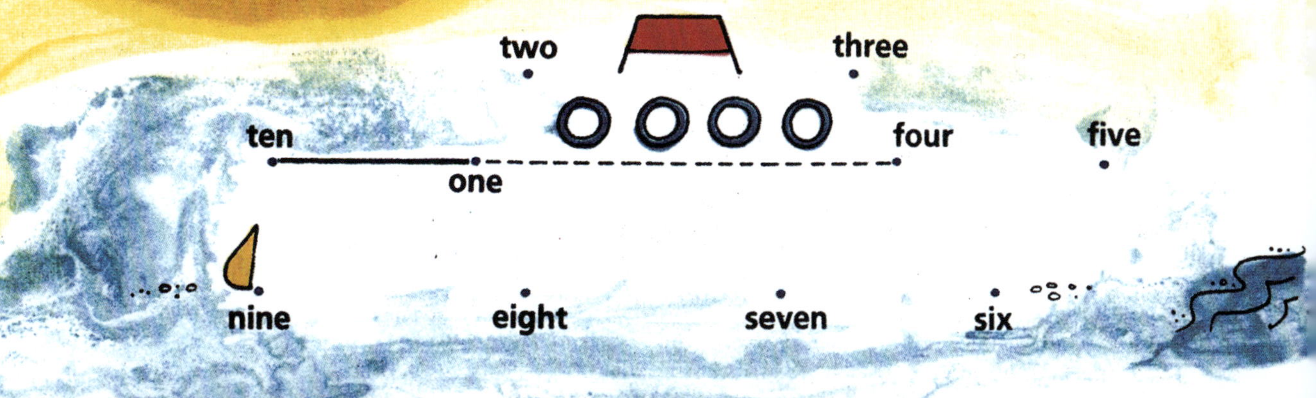

Cooks

2
two
eight
four
ten

six
three
one
five
nine
seven

ten
one
seven
nine
two
eight
six
three
five
four

Colour the first red, the second blue, and the third green.

Match

has a

Sam

Pam

Ali

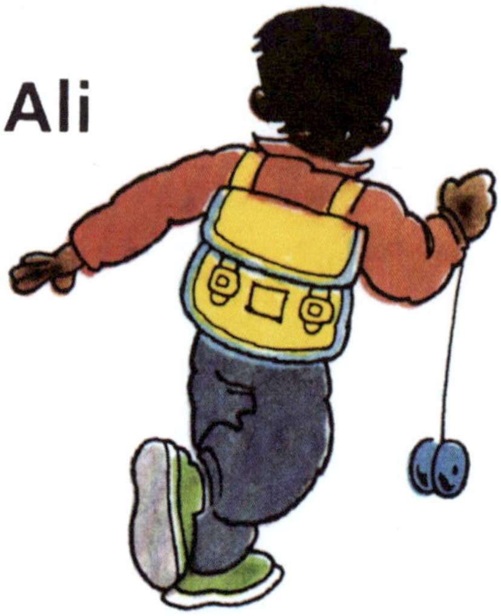

Colour the clothes

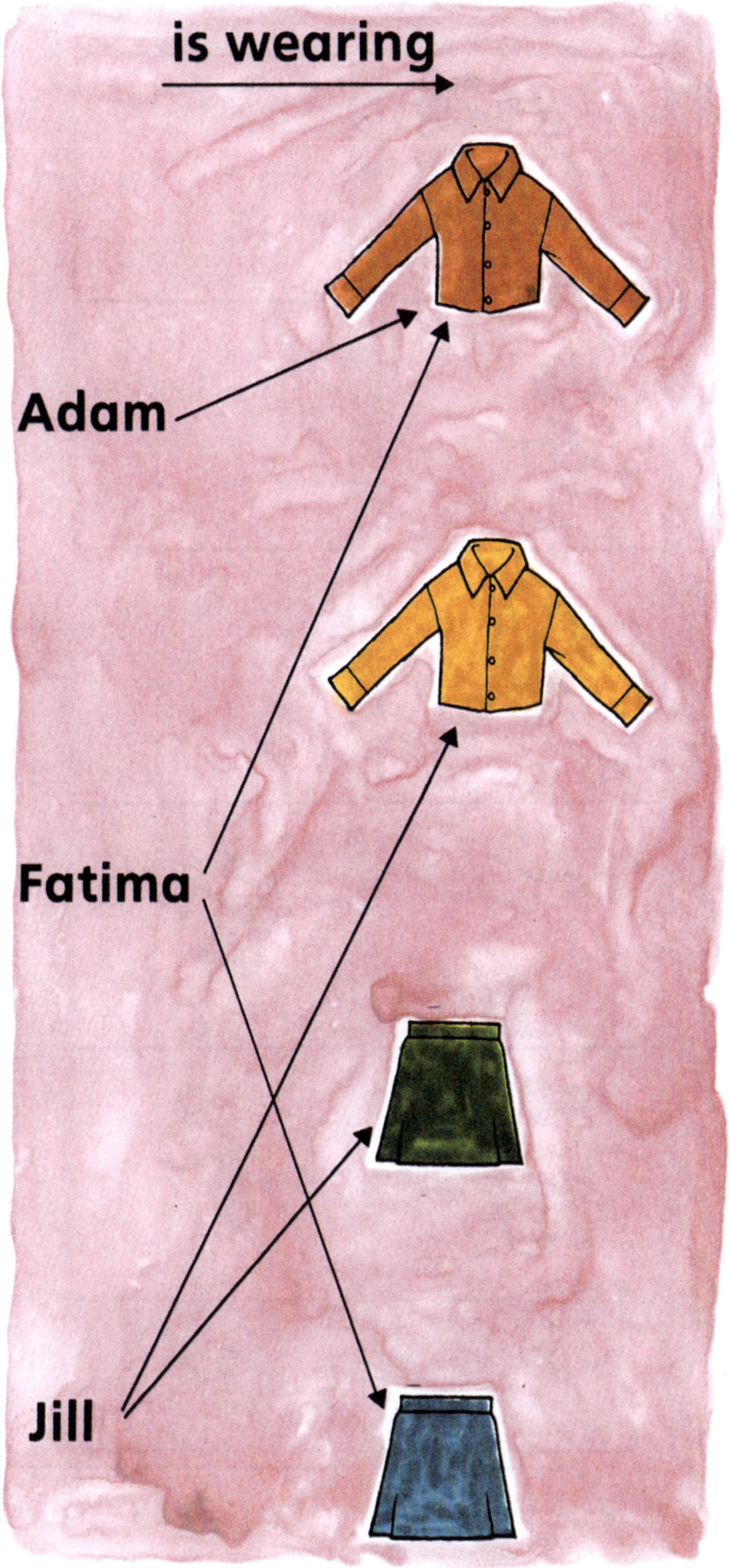

Our group

How many

girls ☐

boys ☐ ?

Draw one more boy.

How many boys now?

☐

Spots

How many?

black spots 2

blue spots

red spots

Draw my **blue** spots
and my **red** spots.

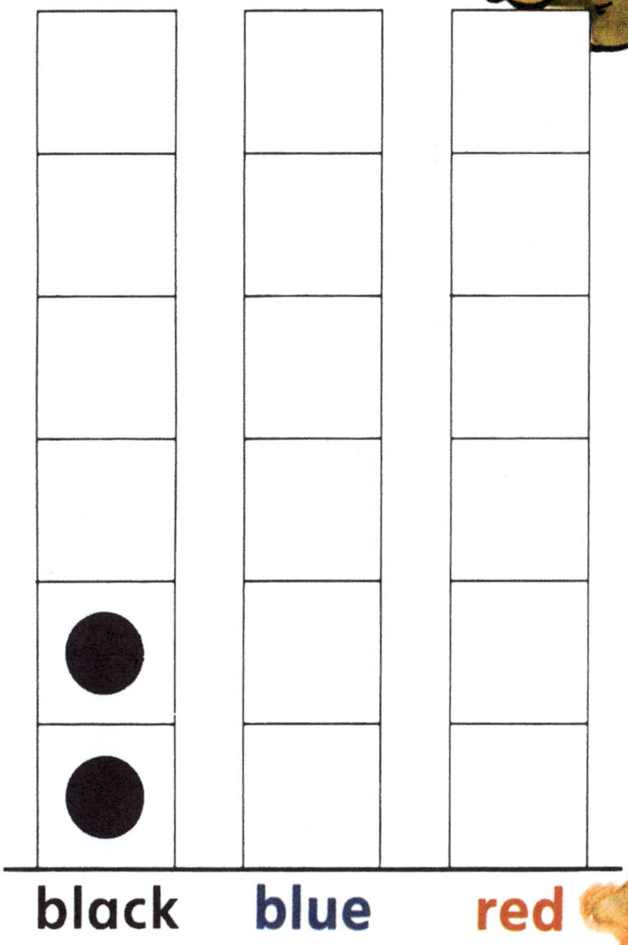

1p coins

Colour 1p coins to buy.

1	2	3	4	5	6	7	8	9	10	11	12	13	14	15

Heinemann is an imprint of Pearson Education Limited, a company incorporated in England and Wales, having its registered office at Edinburgh Gate, Harlow, Essex, CM20 2JE.
Registered company number: 872828
ISBN 978 0 435 03085 8
First published 1991. Revised edition 1995. 22 30
Typeset and illustrated by Oxprint Design.

ISBN 978-0-435030-85-8

SPMG

HEINEMANN MATHEMATICS 1

Name

WORKBOOK 4

Number to 10 : Relationships

Revised

How much?

Bus
ticket
p

Bus ticket
p

Bus ticket
p

Bus
ticket
p

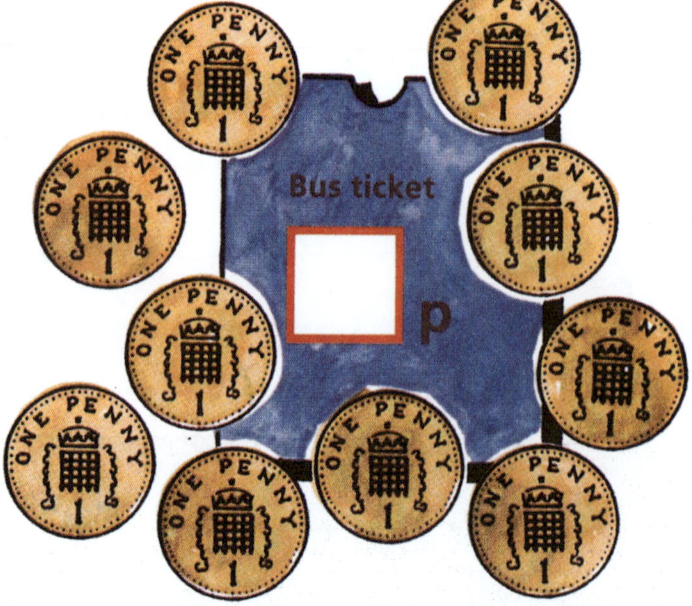
Bus ticket
p

Bus tickets

Jan has ___ p

Can she buy

? ___

Sam has ___ p

Can he buy

? ___

Jess has ___ p

Can she buy

? ___

Join the dots.

1 to 10

Bees

1 2 3 4 5 6 7 8 9 10

Write the number

after 3

after 6

after 9

after 5

before 2

before 8

Flower garden

Ring the one that is different.

On the

beach

How many?

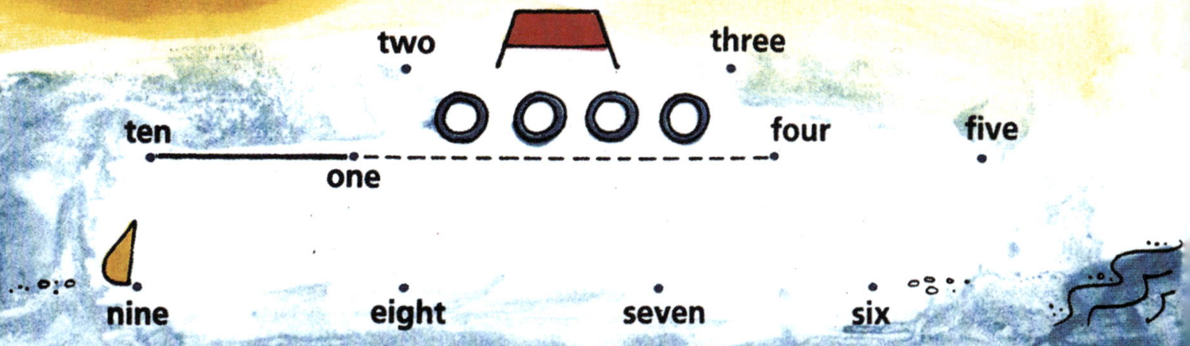

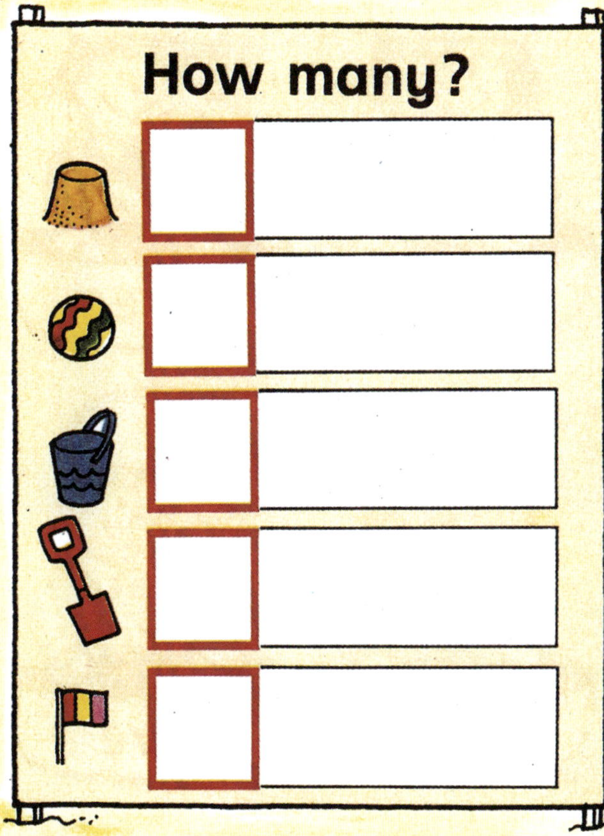

Cooks

2
two
eight
four
ten
six
three
one
five
nine
seven

ten
one
seven
nine
two
eight
six
three
five
four

Colour the first red, the second blue, and the third green.

Match

has a

Sam

Pam

Ali

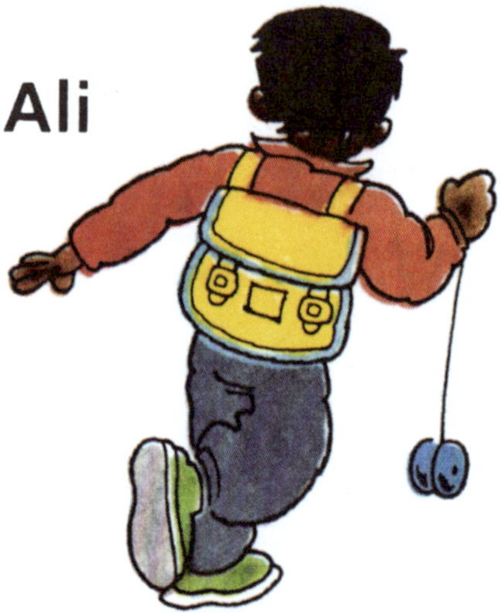

Colour the clothes

Adam

Fatima

Jill

Our group

How many

girls ☐

boys ☐ ?

Draw one more boy.

How many boys now?

☐

Spots

How many?

black spots 2

blue spots

red spots

Draw my **blue** spots and my **red** spots.

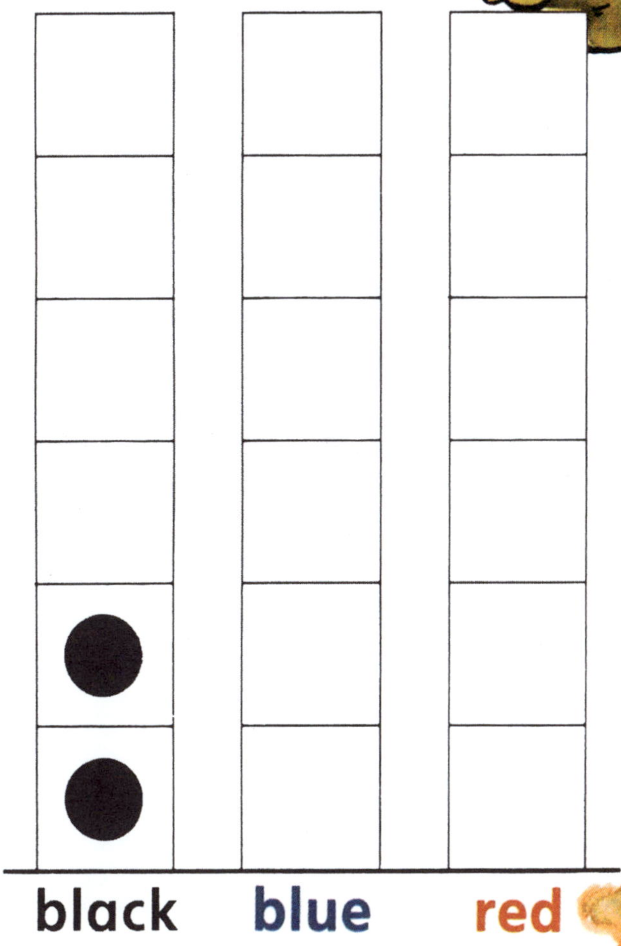

●		
●		
black	blue	red

1p coins

Colour 1p coins to buy.

1	2	3	4	5	6	7	8	9	10	11	12	13	14	15

Heinemann is an imprint of Pearson Education Limited, a company incorporated in England and Wales, having its registered office at Edinburgh Gate, Harlow, Essex, CM20 2JE.
Registered company number: 872828
ISBN 978 0 435 03085 8
First published 1991. Revised edition 1995. 22 30
Typeset and illustrated by Oxprint Design.

ISBN 978-0-435030-85-8

SPMG

HEINEMANN MATHEMATICS 1

Name

WORKBOOK 4

Number to 10 : Relationships

Revised

How much?

Bus ticket
p

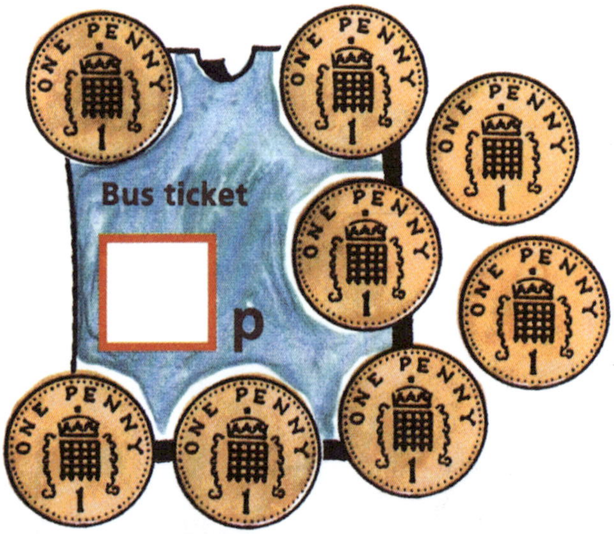
Bus ticket
p

Bus ticket
p

Bus ticket
p

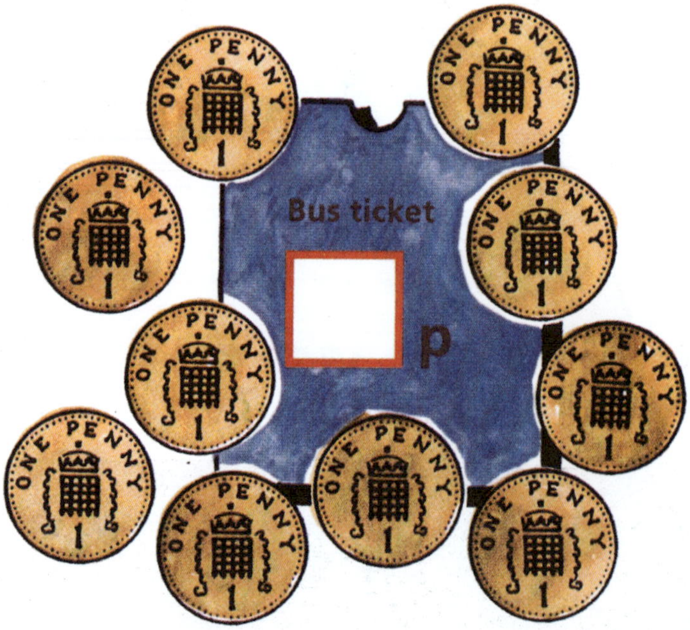
Bus ticket
p

Bus tickets

Jan has [ ] p

Can she buy Bus ticket 7 p ? [ ]

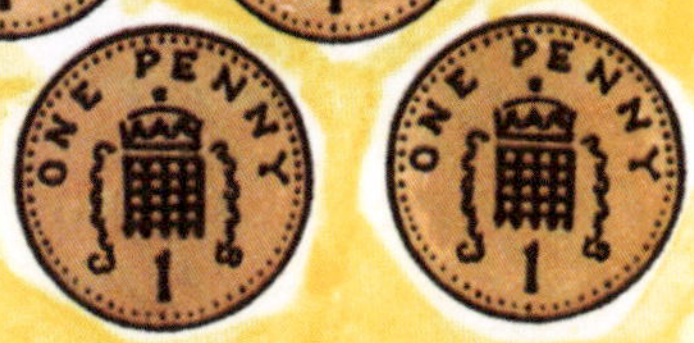

Sam has [ ] p

Can he buy Bus ticket 8 p ? [ ]

Jess has [ ] p

Can she buy Bus ticket 10 p ? [ ]

Join the dots.

1 to 10

Bees

1 2 3 4 5 6 7 8 9 10

Write the number

after 3

after 6

after 9

after 5

before 2

before 8

Flower garden

Ring the one that is different.

On the

beach

6	7	8	9	10
six	seven	eight	nine	ten

How many?

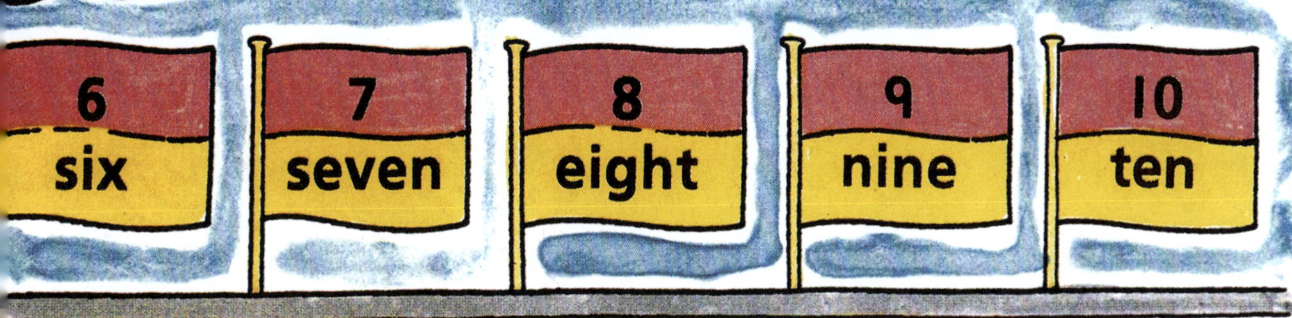

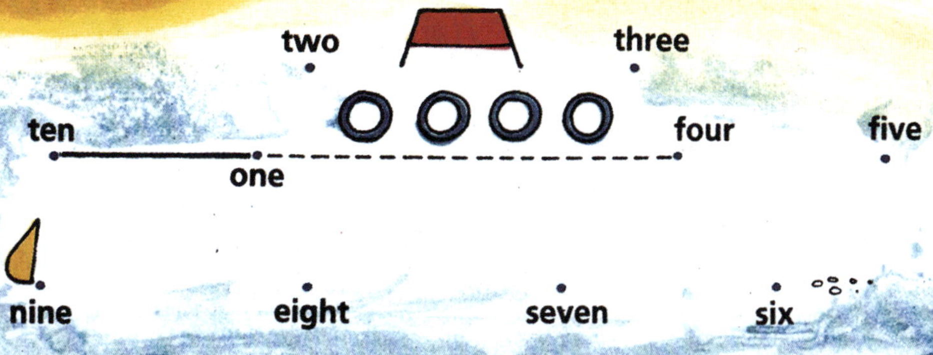

Cooks

2
two
eight
four
ten
six
three
one
five
nine
seven

ten
one
seven
nine
two
eight
six
three
five
four

Colour the first red, the second blue, and the third green.

Match

has a

Sam

Pam

Ali

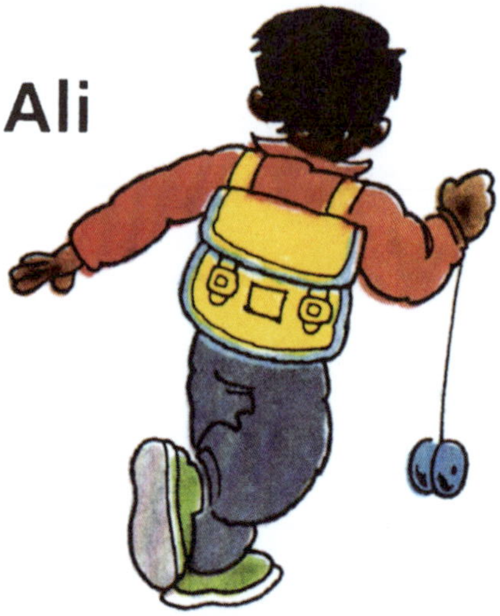

Colour the clothes

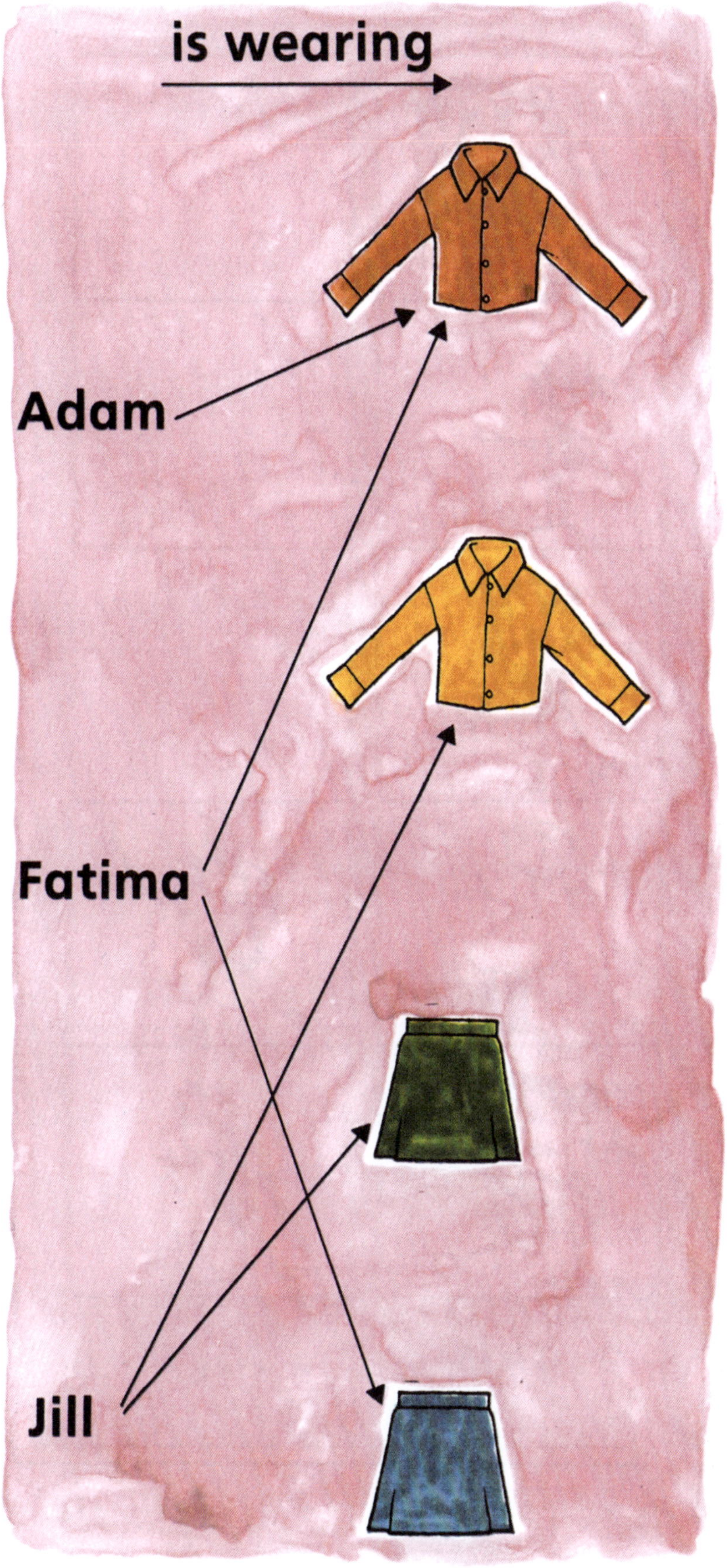

Adam

Fatima

Jill

Our group

How many

girls ☐

boys ☐ ?

Draw one more boy.

How many boys now?

☐

Spots

How many?

black spots 2

blue spots

red spots

Draw my blue spots and my red spots.

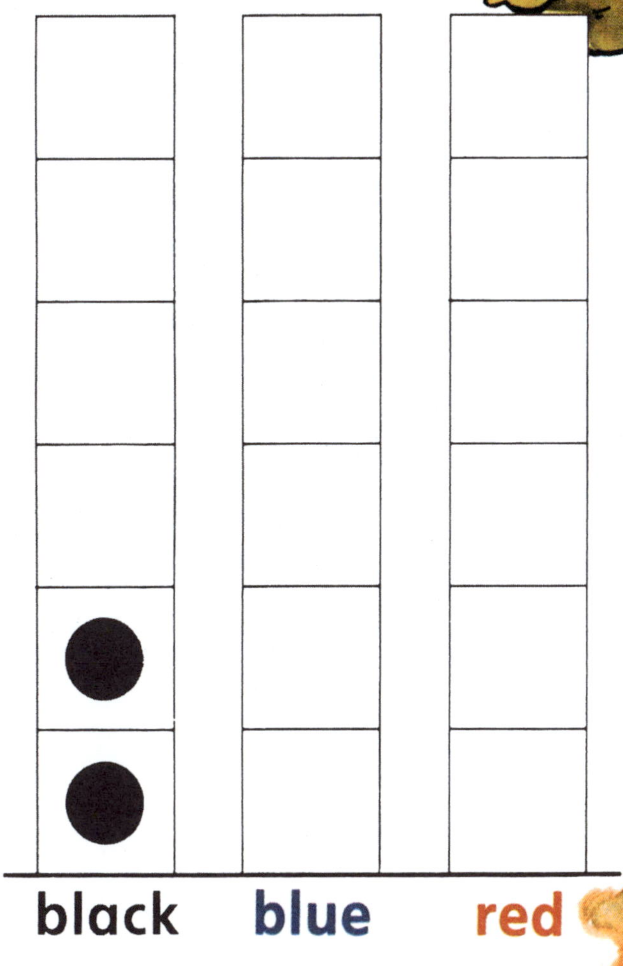

black	blue	red
●		
●		

1p coins

Colour 1p coins to buy.

1	2	3	4	5	6	7	8	9	10	11	12	13	14	15

Heinemann is an imprint of Pearson Education Limited, a company incorporated in England and Wales, having its registered office at Edinburgh Gate, Harlow, Essex, CM20 2JE.
Registered company number: 872828
ISBN 978 0 435 03085 8
First published 1991. Revised edition 1995. 22 30
Typeset and illustrated by Oxprint Design.

ISBN 978-0-435030-85-8

SPMG

HEINEMANN MATHEMATICS 1

Name

WORKBOOK 4

Number to 10 : Relationships

Revised

How much?

Bus
ticket
p

Bus ticket
p

Bus ticket
p

Bus
ticket
p

Bus ticket
p

Bus tickets

Jan has ☐ p

Can she buy ? ☐

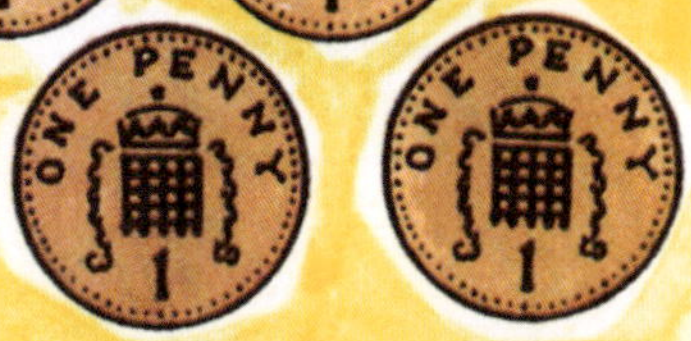

Sam has ☐ p

Can he buy ? ☐

Jess has ☐ p

Can she buy ? ☐

Join the dots.

1 to 10

Bees

1 2 3 4 5 6 7 8 9 10

Write the number

Flower garden

Ring the one that is different.

On the

beach

How many?

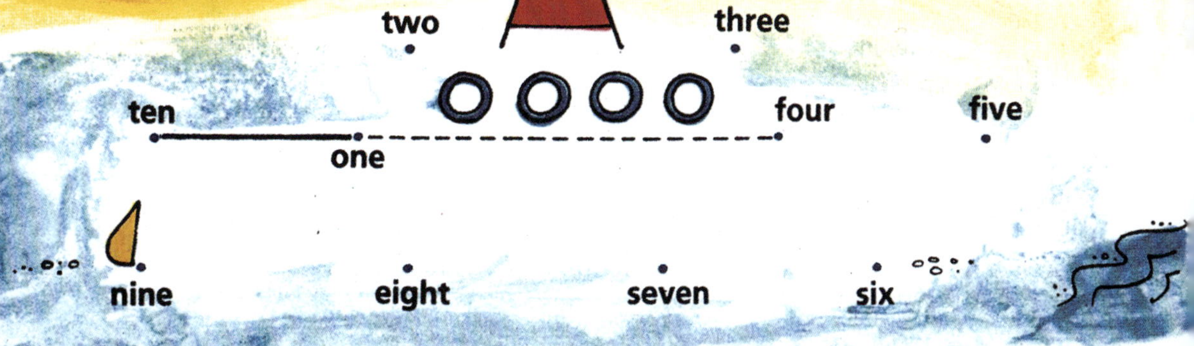

Cooks

2
two
eight
four
ten
six
three
one
five
nine
seven

ten
one
seven
nine
two
eight
three
six
five
four

Colour the first red, the second blue, and the third green.

Match

has a

Sam

Pam

Ali

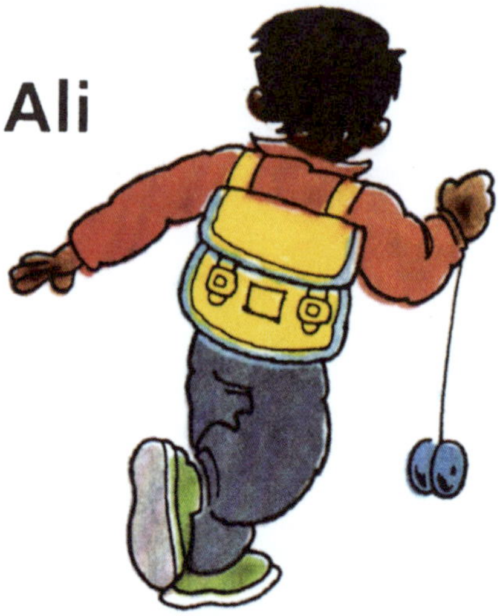

Colour the clothes

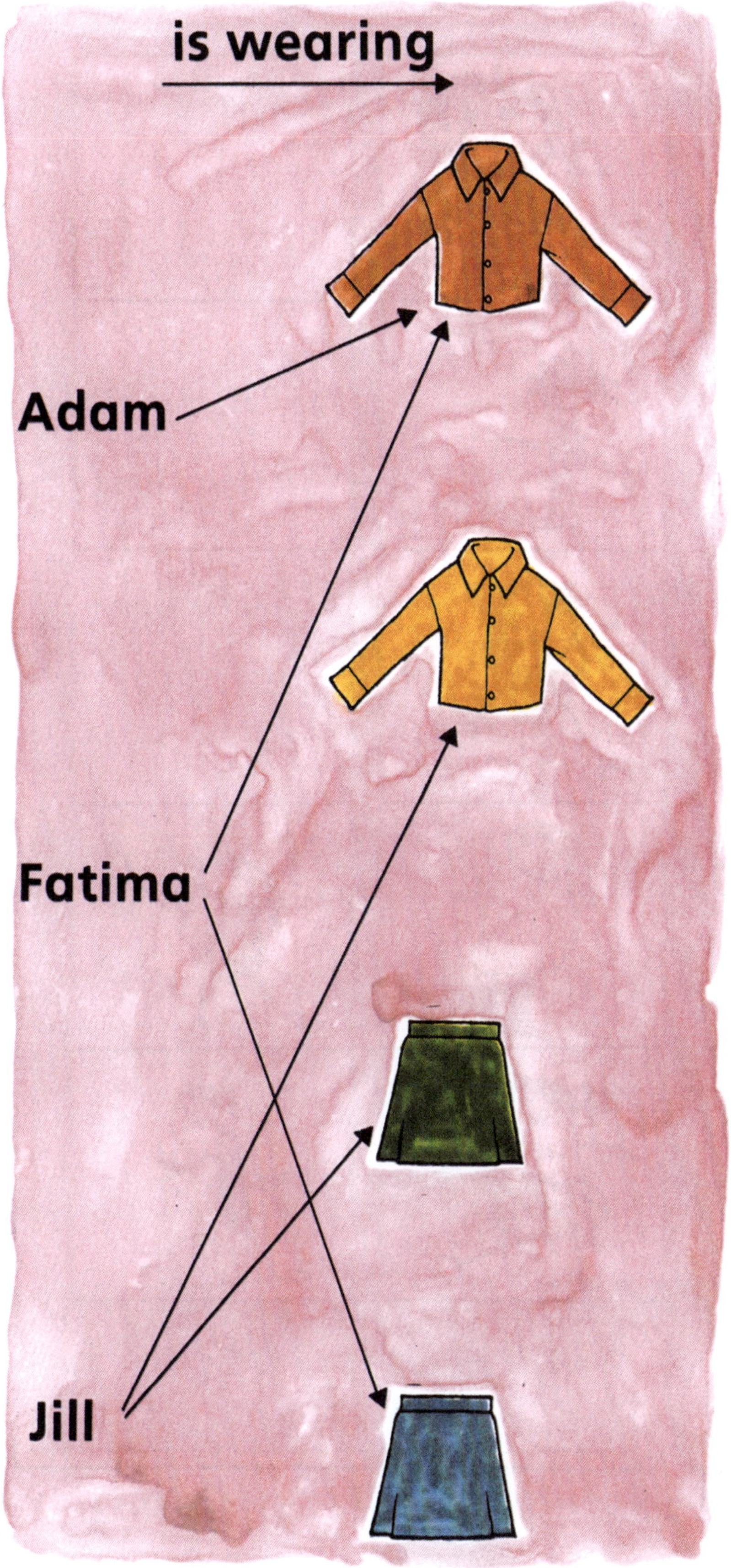

Our group

How many

girls ☐

boys ☐ ?

Draw one more boy.

How many boys now?

☐

Spots

How many?

black spots	2
blue spots	
red spots	

Draw my blue spots and my red spots.

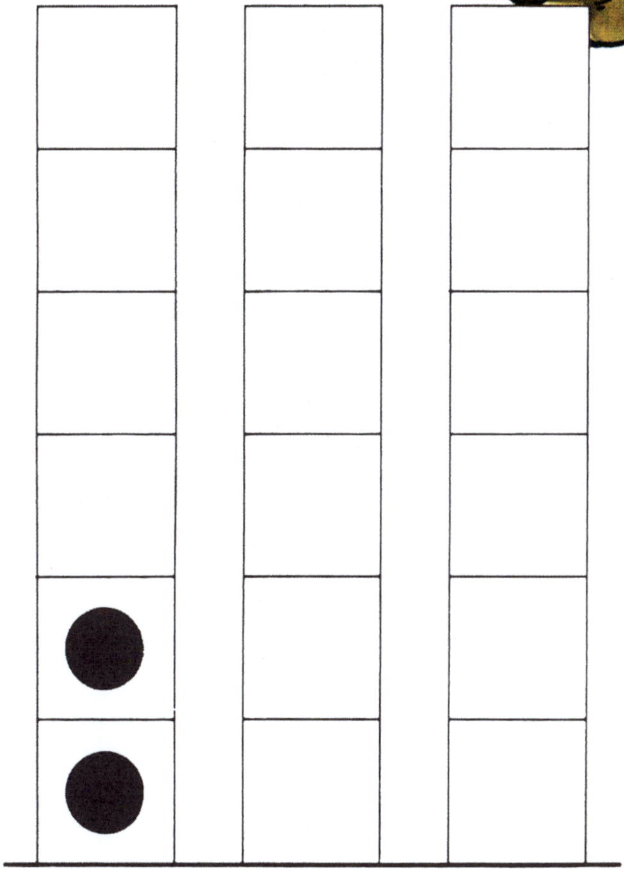

black blue red

1p coins

Colour 1p coins to buy.

1	2	3	4	5	6	7	8	9	10	11	12	13	14	15

Heinemann is an imprint of Pearson Education Limited, a company incorporated in England and Wales, having its registered office at Edinburgh Gate, Harlow, Essex, CM20 2JE.
Registered company number: 872828
ISBN 978 0 435 03085 8 © Scottish Primary Mathematics Group 1991.
First published 1991. Revised edition 1995. 22 30
Typeset and illustrated by Oxprint Design.

ISBN 978-0-435030-85-8

SPMG

HEINEMANN MATHEMATICS 1

Name

WORKBOOK 4

Number to 10 : Relationships

Revised

How much?

Bus
ticket
p

Bus ticket
p

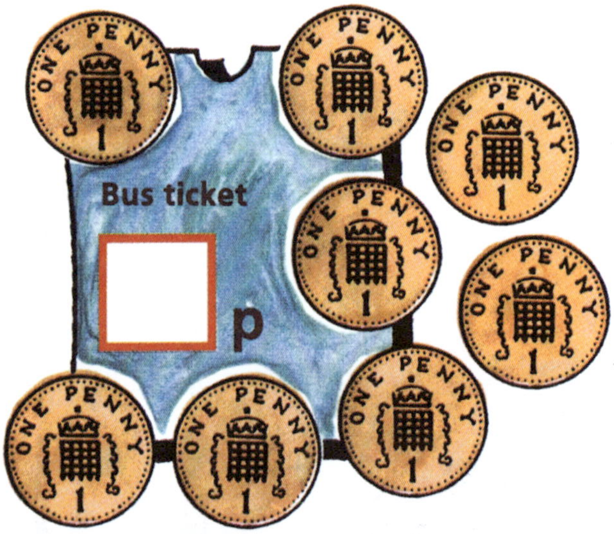
Bus ticket
p

Bus
ticket
p

Bus ticket
p

Bus tickets

Jan has ☐ p

Can she buy 

? ☐

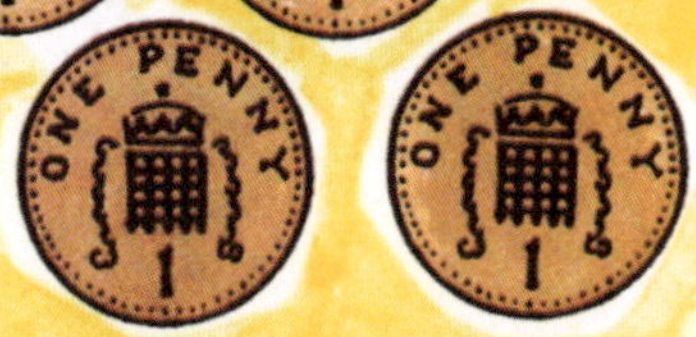

Sam has ☐ p

Can he buy 

? ☐

Jess has ☐ p

Can she buy 

? ☐

Join the dots.

1 to 10

Bees

1 2 3 4 5 6 7 8 9 10

Write the number

after 3

after 6

after 9

after 5

before 2

before 8

Flower garden

Ring the one that is different.

On the

beach

How many?

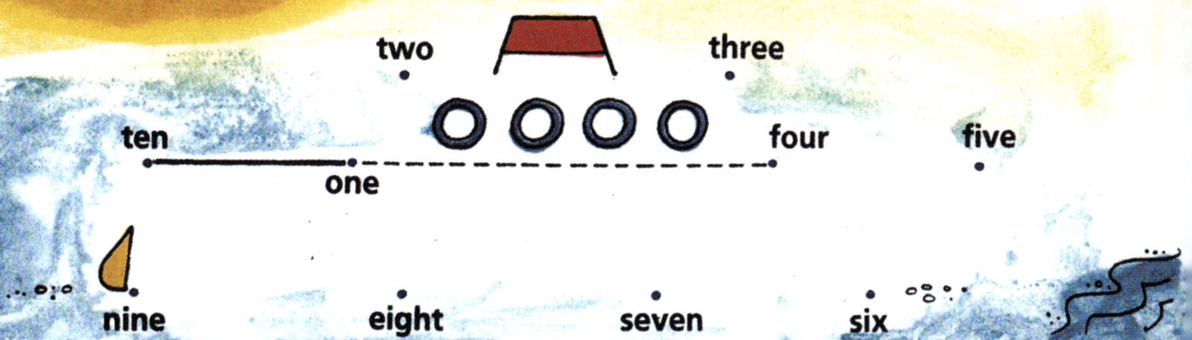

Cooks

2
two
eight
four
ten
six
three
one
five
nine
seven

ten
one
seven
nine
two
eight
six
three
five
four

Colour the first red, the second blue, and the third green.

Match

has a →

Sam

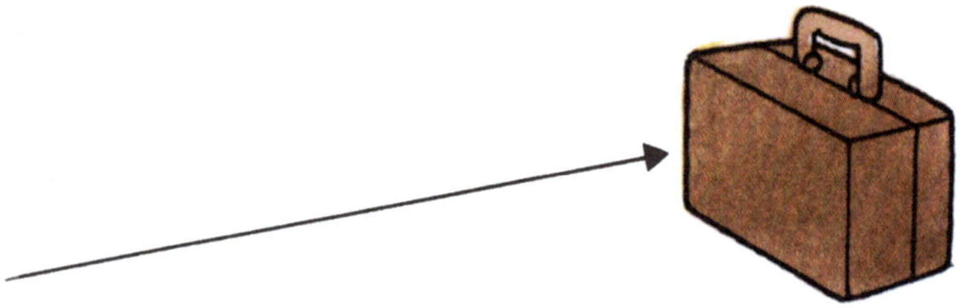

Pam

Ali

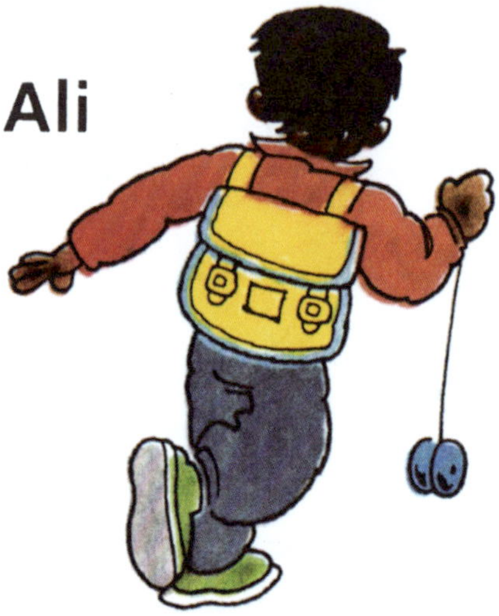

Colour the clothes

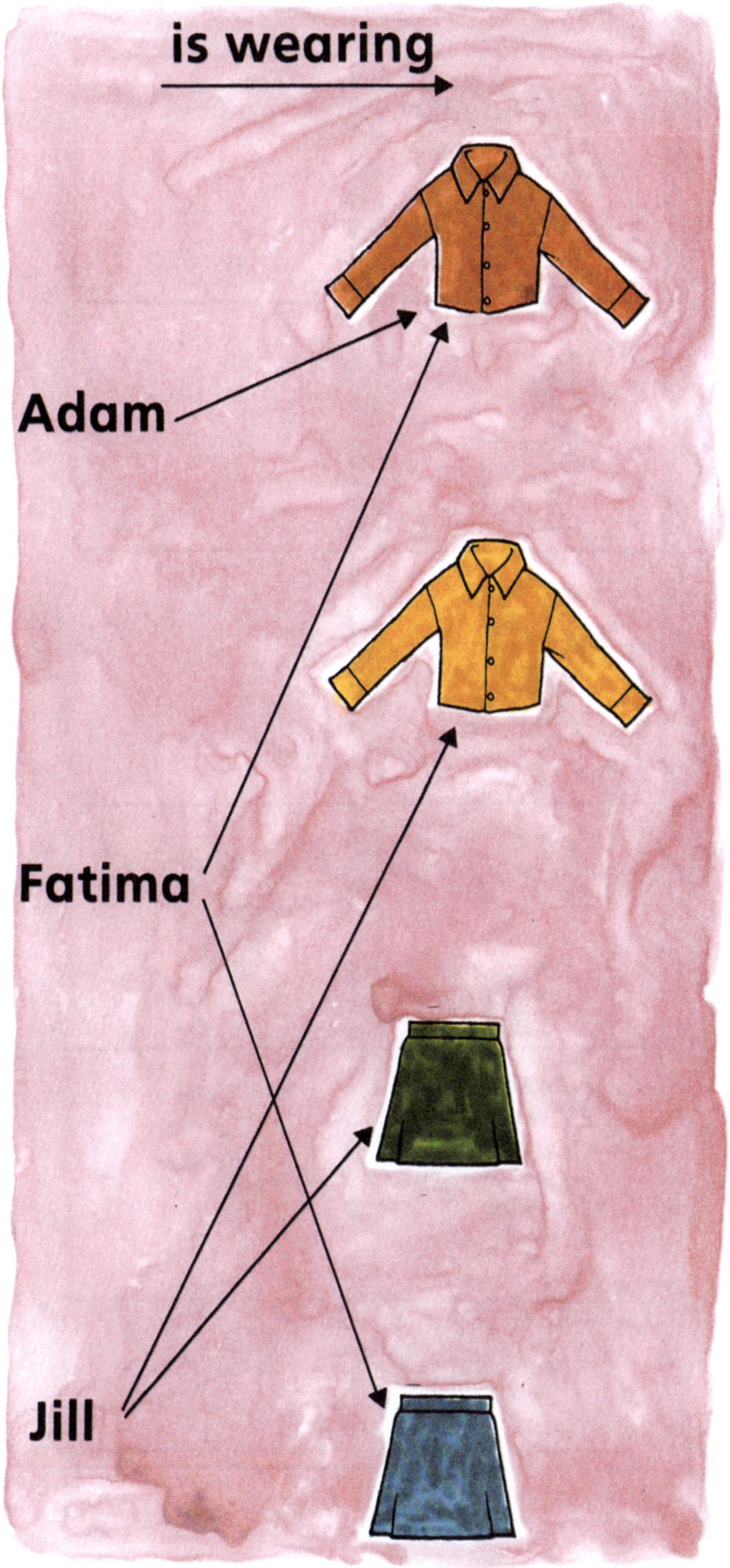

Our group

How many

girls ☐

boys ☐ ?

Draw one more boy.

How many boys now?

☐

Spots

How many?

black spots **2**

blue spots

red spots

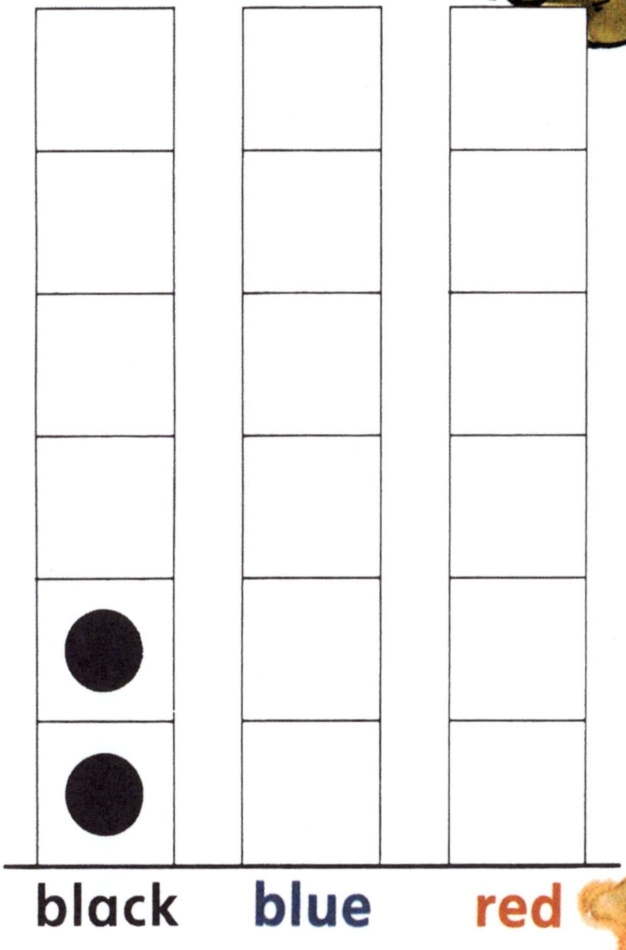

1p coins

Colour 1p coins to buy.

1	2	3	4	5	6	7	8	9	10	11	12	13	14	15

Heinemann is an imprint of Pearson Education Limited, a company incorporated in England and Wales, having its registered office at Edinburgh Gate, Harlow, Essex, CM20 2JE.
Registered company number: 872828
ISBN 978 0 435 03085 8
First published 1991. Revised edition 1995. 22 30
Typeset and illustrated by Oxprint Design.

ISBN 978-0-435030-85-8

SPMG

HEINEMANN MATHEMATICS 1

Name

WORKBOOK 4

Number to 10 : Relationships

Revised

How much?

Bus ticket
p

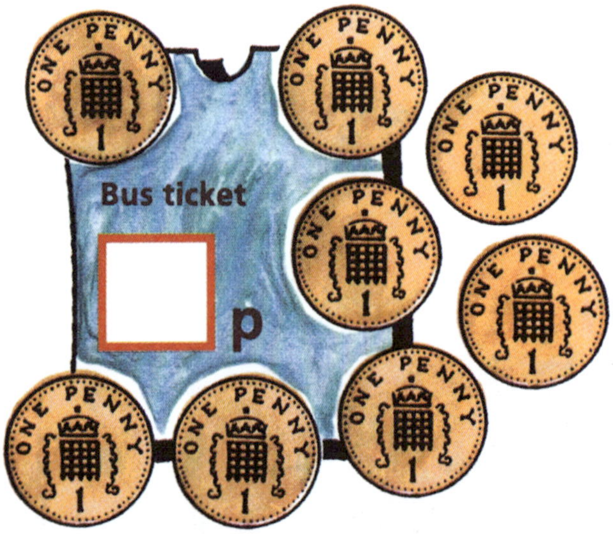
Bus ticket
p

Bus ticket
p

Bus ticket
p

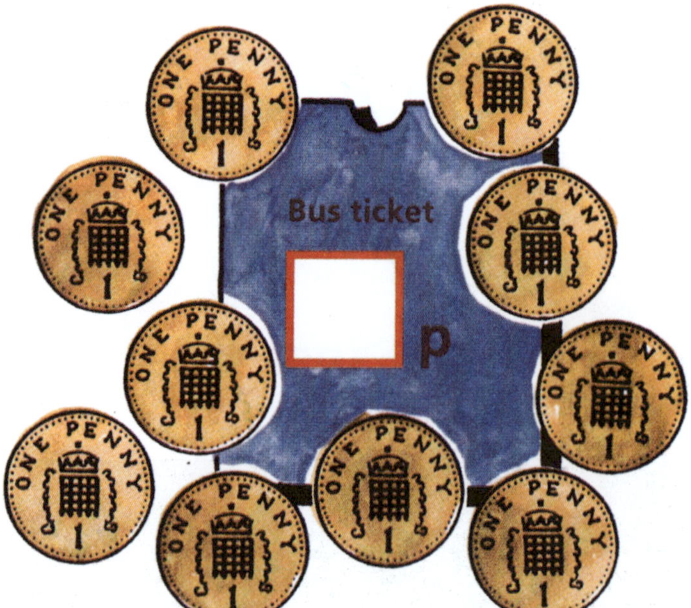
Bus ticket
p

Bus tickets

Jan has ☐ p

Can she buy 

? ☐

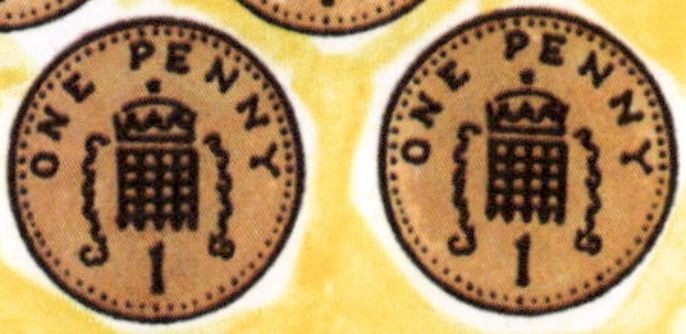

Sam has ☐ p

Can he buy 

? ☐

Jess has ☐ p

Can she buy 

? ☐

Join the dots.

1 to 10

Bees

1 2 3 4 5 6 7 8 9 10

Write the number

Flower garden

Ring the one that is different.

On the

beach

6	7	8	9	10
six	seven	eight	nine	ten

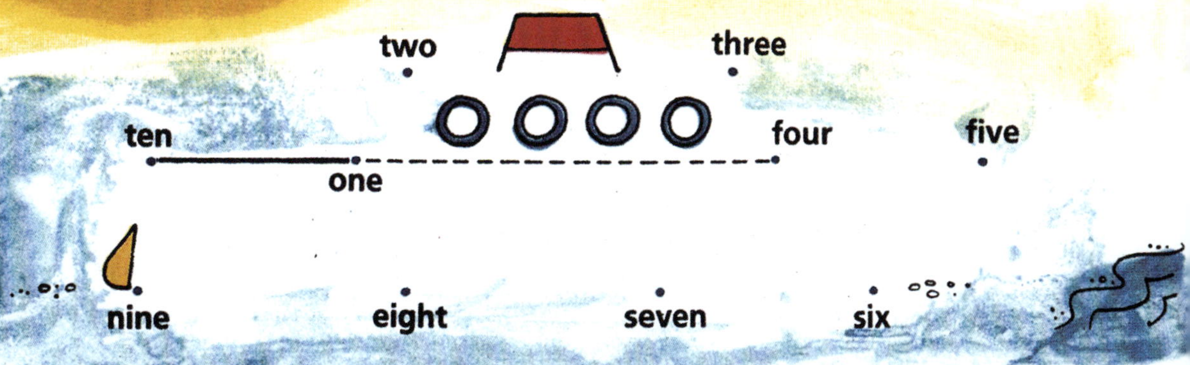

Cooks

2
two
eight
four
ten
six
three
one
five
nine
seven

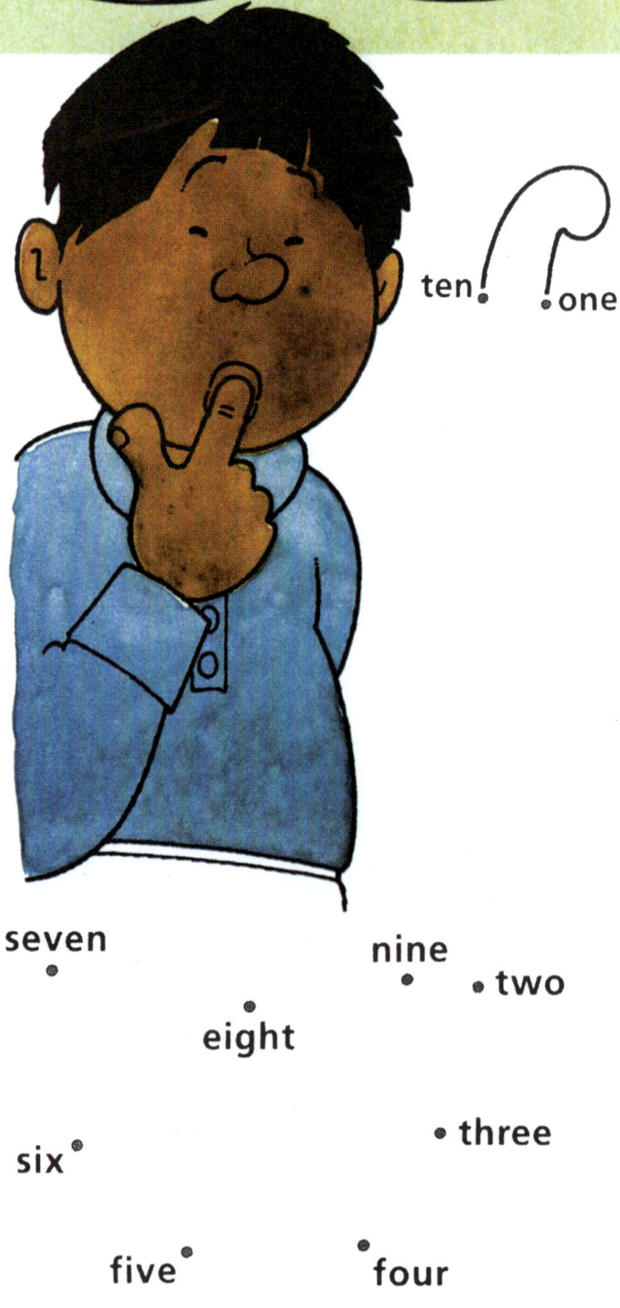
ten
one
seven
nine
two
eight
three
six
five
four

Colour the first red, the second blue, and the third green.

Match

has a →

Sam

Pam

Ali

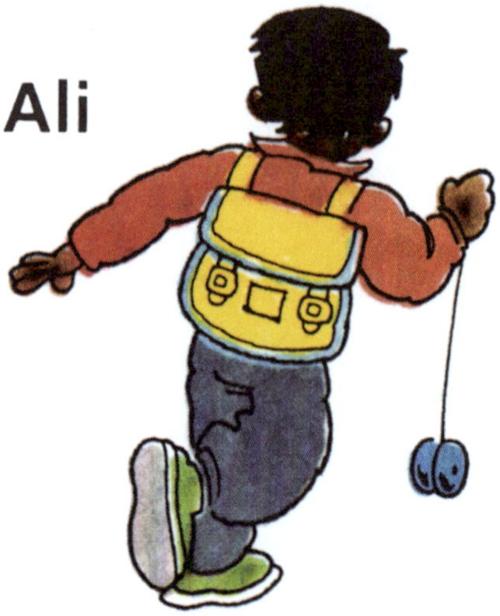

Colour the clothes

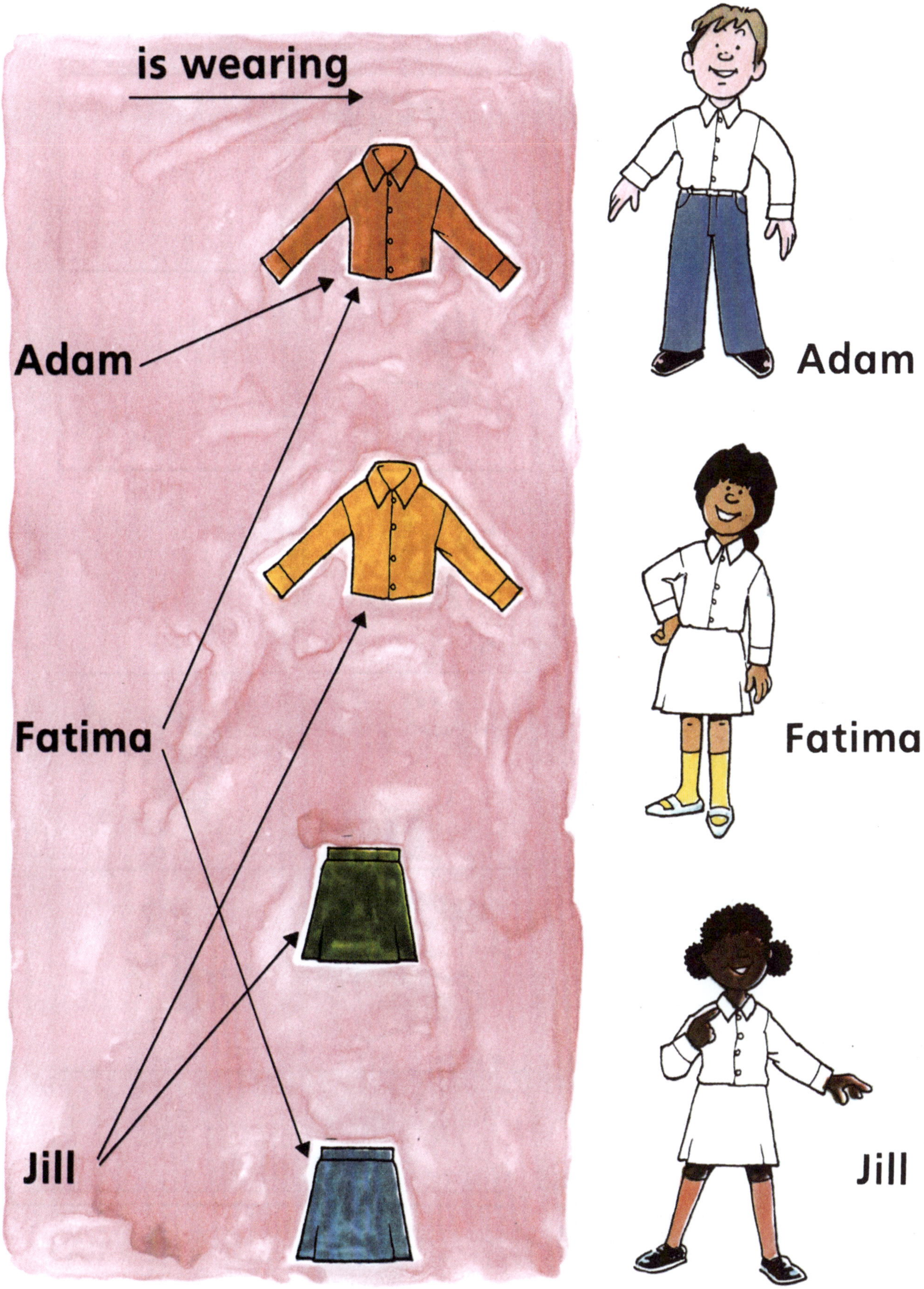

Our group

How many

girls ☐

boys ☐ ?

Draw one more boy.

How many boys now?

☐

Spots

How many?

black spots 2

blue spots

red spots

Draw my blue spots and my red spots.

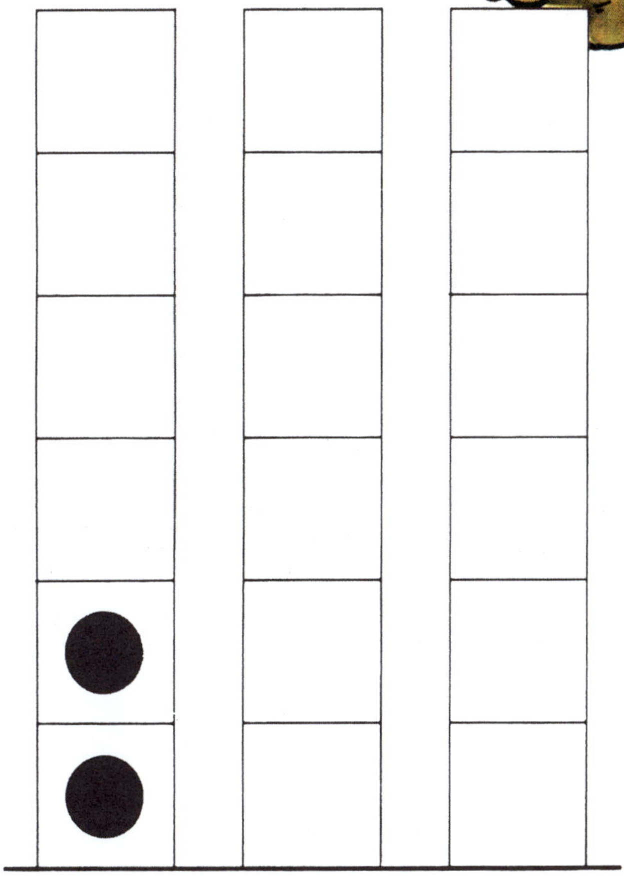

black blue red

1p coins

Colour 1p coins to buy.

1	2	3	4	5	6	7	8	9	10	11	12	13	14	15

Heinemann is an imprint of Pearson Education Limited, a company incorporated in England and Wales, having its registered office at Edinburgh Gate, Harlow, Essex, CM20 2JE.
Registered company number: 872828
ISBN 978 0 435 03085 8
First published 1991. Revised edition 1995. 22 30
Typeset and illustrated by Oxprint Design.

ISBN 978-0-435030-85-8